Cherry blossom Cat

Written by Tony Langham
Illustrated by Lynne Willey

Heinemann

Chapter 1

Tabitha was a travelling cat. She was always on the move. She was always looking for new places to go and new people to see.

One day Tabitha got on a plane without anyone seeing her and went all the way to Japan.

In Japan lived an old lady called
Mrs Koyama. She had a beautiful
garden with lots of lovely plants,
but the one she loved best of all was a
cherry blossom tree. The tree was very
old and it had beautiful pink blossom.

One day Mrs Koyama was in her garden when she heard a noise.
She looked in the herb garden.
Nothing there.

She looked in the vegetable garden.
Nothing there.

Then she heard the noise again. It was coming from the cherry blossom tree.
There, behind the tree, Mrs Koyama saw Tabitha.

Tabitha had hurt her paw. She had
cut it on some glass in the street
outside Mrs Koyama's house.
'Meow!' went Tabitha when she saw
Mrs Koyama.
'You poor thing,' said Mrs Koyama
when she saw Tabitha. 'Does it hurt?'
'Meow!' went Tabitha again.

Very carefully Mrs Koyama picked
Tabitha up and took her into her house.
She put Tabitha down on the kitchen
table. Then she got some cotton wool
and a little bowl of warm water.
Mrs Koyama cleaned Tabitha's paw,
put some cream on it and then she put
a bandage on it.

Next Mrs Koyama made Tabitha a
bed out of a cardboard box.

'Now you must sleep,' she said, and
she turned off the light.

Tabitha was very tired. She had
walked a long way that day and soon
she was fast asleep.

The next day Mrs Koyama gave
Tabitha some milk. Then she put
Tabitha in a box and carried her out to
the garden. She put the box down under
the cherry blossom tree, and then she
got on with her work.

A little while later Mrs Koyama put
Tabitha in a big basket and took her to
the market to buy fish, fruit and rice.
When she had got everything she
needed, they went back home again.

Tabitha stayed with Mrs Koyama and every day her paw got better and better. Soon she was walking as well as she always did, and she started to go out for walks on her own.

Chapter 2

One day, when Tabitha came back
from one of her walks, she could not
see Mrs Koyama out in the garden.

She looked in
the herb garden.

She looked in the
vegetable garden.
But she could not
find her.

Then Tabitha heard a noise. She ran
into the house and there she saw
Mrs Koyama on the kitchen floor.
Tabitha ran over to her.
'Meow!' she went, but Mrs Koyama's
eyes were shut and she did not move.
Tabitha saw a stool on its side.
Mrs Koyama must have fallen off
the stool.

Tabitha ran out of the house to get some help. She ran as quickly as she could to the next house down the street.

'Meow!' she went, but no one came.

Then Tabitha ran on to the next house.
'Meow! Meow!' she went, as loudly
as she could.
But still no one came.

'Meow! Meow! Meow!' went Tabitha,
even louder at the next house.
And this time there was someone there.
Tabitha could hear someone moving
about. The door was open so Tabitha
went in.

Tabitha saw a man in the room.
'MEOW!' went Tabitha.
The man turned round.
'Shoo!' he said. 'Get out!'
But Tabitha did not move.
'Get out! Get out!' said the man again.
But still Tabitha would not move. Then
Tabitha saw a gold ring on a table. She
jumped up, picked up the ring and ran
out of the house with it in her mouth.

Tabitha ran down the road and the
man chased after her.
'Come back! Put that down, you
bad cat!' he shouted.
But Tabitha went on running all the
way back to Mrs Koyama's house.

She ran back into the kitchen and put
the ring down next to Mrs Koyama.

Just then the man ran into the kitchen
and saw Mrs Koyama on the floor.
He forgot all about his ring and went
over to the phone to call for an
ambulance.

Soon the ambulance came and took
Mrs Koyama away. When she had
gone, Tabitha picked up the ring and
gave it back to the man.
'Thank you,' said the man. 'What a
clever cat you are! You can come and
stay with me while Mrs Koyama
is away.'

When Mrs Koyama came home again the man took Tabitha back. He told Mrs Koyama all about the ring and how Tabitha had run for help.
'Thank you, cat,' said Mrs Koyama.
'You are very clever.'

When the man had gone, Mrs Koyama
took Tabitha out into the garden.
She sat down under the cherry blossom
tree and put Tabitha next to her
in her box.

'Later I will go to the market and
buy you a big fish,' Mrs Koyama said
to Tabitha. 'You would like that,
wouldn't you?'
But when Mrs Koyama looked down,
Tabitha had gone. She never stayed
in one place for long because
Tabitha was a travelling cat.